# THIS IS SYLVIA

*"The truth about myself, unvarnished and unadorned"*

# THIS IS SYLVIA

## HER LIVES AND LOVES

### Written and Illustrated by
# Sandy Wilson

E. P. DUTTON & CO., INC.

NEW YORK                    1955

Library of Congress Number 55-6512

AMERICAN BOOK–STRATFORD PRESS, INC., NEW YORK

*To JON*
*who is allowed*
*to call her Syl*

# CONTENTS

*with 54 line drawings by the author*

# THIS IS SYLVIA

# CHAPTER I

## *The tail begins*

I have often been urged to write my memoirs. "Sylvia," my friends would say, "of all the cats we know, yours has been the most eventful career. You have lived your nine lives to the full. Why not give your story to the public?"

But I hesitated. For I have, in the course of my adventures, been involved with many famous cats, some of whom might not relish the thought of their associations with me being related in print. There was, for instance, my first husband, who is a member of one of England's oldest aristocratic families. Our marriage and subsequent divorce caused an upheaval in London society which some people might consider best forgotten. Then there was the famous Hollywood star who was my rival, not only on celluloid but in private life as well. And in more recent years my name has been associated with various political figures who still hold positions of prominence in the Government—in fact, in one case, it was I who, believe it or not, was largely responsible for securing that position. But that was, and must remain, a close secret.

So, as I have said, I hesitated to commit my story to paper until just recently, when I had a long conversation with my friend and mentor (or should I say mentrix?), Hester Briggs, who has so often guided me in my career. I will not repeat it in full, but it ended with her saying to me:

"Sylvia, my love, you have settled down at last.

You are comfortably married, and your children are well cared for. Now, while you have the leisure and before you start forgetting things, why don't you write your memoirs? Everyone is waiting for them, and if they cause repercussions, you've got nothing to fear. Your position is secure. Go ahead, do it—if only to please your old friend Hester, who gave you a start in the world when you were a mere kitten."

Such an appeal could hardly be disregarded. So I have finally taken the plunge, and here, for all to read and make of them what they will, are my memoirs.

✳     ✳     ✳

My mother was, I should say, the most beautiful cat of her day. And she was, unlike myself, of a pure Persian strain. In fact her great-grandfather was a Sultan, whose daughter, my great-grandmother, contracted a marriage with an Anglo-Persian aristocrat whom she met while he was on a mouse-hunting expedition in Persia. He took her home to his estate just outside Catford, and there she bore him several families. The portrait of my great-grandparents surrounded by some of their children is one of the most famous paintings in the cat world, and I have accordingly included a reproduction of it (rather an inferior one, I'm afraid!) in this book. My grandmother is standing on the left, and, as will be seen, she was also possessed of extraordinary good looks. She was in due course married to the eldest son of a neighbouring family, Lord Herrington of Hakeworth, her wedding being the main social event of the year; and just nine

Mother's great-grandfather was a Sultan

*My great-grandparents' family portrait*

weeks later she gave birth to five kittens, three girls and two boys, the last to appear being my mother, who was christened Yasmin, after my celebrated great-grandmother.

It was of course intended that my mother should also marry a pure Persian and thus help to perpetuate the family strain. But, to my grandparents' regret, she became involved with a set which was known in its day as the Bright Young Cats. My mother had always been of an artistic frame of mind—she went in for water-colours while at school—and this inclined her towards the more Bohemian circles of Society. I never discussed this period much with her—in fact she and I very rarely discussed anything; but she would occasionally drop hints about wild parties at which cream flowed like water, and I have managed to secure a snap of her taken at this time, which indicates that she had wandered rather far from the staid environs of her family at Hakeworth.

*Mother in her younger days*

I must confess that in my youth, when I first discovered that my Persian strain was not as strong as
it might have been, I was inclined to resent the indis-
cretion that had caused Mother to become involved
with my father, who must, I am forced to conclude,
have been a perfectly ordinary tabby with a dash of
ginger. But Hester Briggs, to whom, as I have already
said, I owe so much, was quick to correct my mistaken
attitude.

"You should be thankful," she told me one day,
when I was feeling particularly depressed about my
origins. "Half-breeds always have the best of both
worlds. Look at the Empress J—— who was half black
and half white. She rose to heights which a mere pure
white cat would never have attained. You are destined
for great things, Sylvia. If your mother had lived the
life her parents wanted her to, you would now be a
dull country cat with nothing to look forward to but

*A tattered handbill*

endless families of kittens. But as it is, I'm perfectly certain you're going to have a career such as it is given to few cats to enjoy."

How right she was!

# CHAPTER II

## *My friend Hester*

My mother's marriage, as my grandparents prophesied, did not last. My father, whom I scarcely knew, had, as I have said, a streak of ginger—a colour which usually stands in the cat world for a roving disposition, among other things. I am not even sure what profession, if any, my father followed, my only clue being a tattered handbill which I found amongst Mother's possessions and which I have reproduced in these pages. If this was indeed her husband, then it explains my natural aptitude for the drama. Mother, as far as I know, never appeared on the stage, though I believe she was often called upon to sing at the parties I mentioned in the previous chapter, her special party piece being a rendition of "Three Little Fishes" accompanied by herself on the banjo, which always went down very well. I can also remember her singing me to sleep with a popular song of my childhood, "I'm Dreaming of a Whiting Dinner", and her voice, though small, was very sweet.

But that is a memory of my childhood. As I approached my teens, Mother became less and less in evidence and I was usually left to my own devices. I believe it was intended that I should go to Rodine College for Girl Cats, but somehow funds were never sufficient; and as Mother never bothered to keep in touch with her parents at Hakeworth, they were disinclined to pay out good money for a granddaughter they never saw.

It was at this point that Hester Briggs came into the picture. Dear Hester, what a friend she has been to me! I shall never forget that afternoon when she rang the doorbell of our tiny flat in Pimlico and discovered me in tears over a piece of cod which I was trying to prepare for supper, Mother having gone out to an afternoon crab-and-cream party in Chelsea. It turned out that Hester had been a great friend of Mother's in her youth, but had gone abroad during the Slump and opened a fish restaurant in Famagusta. She had only returned the previous day, having saved up enough money to retire to Dolphin Square, and Mother was the first friend she had decided to call on. She had no idea of my existence, but she told me that as soon as she set eyes on me, dishevelled as I was, my eyes red with weeping over the ruined cod, she took me to her heart. In fact she invited me there and then to have tea with

*In tears over a piece of cod*

her at Slater's, and before long I was seeing her every day and incidentally beginning to receive from her an education which I am sure has been far more useful to me than anything I could have learned at Rodine.

As will be seen from her photograph, Hester Briggs must have been extremely pretty in her younger days. Indeed she was a central figure in the period of the Bright Young Cats, and when she finally attained her ambition by opening her own drinking and dancing establishment, the Kitty-Kat Club, all Society flocked to enjoy her hospitality and hear her entertain. I remember Mother had a record of Hester singing a popular hit of the period, "Bye, Bye, Blackbird", and I believe she would perform this song with the aid of a heavily bejewelled mechanical blackbird by Fabergé, which would hop from table to table among

*Hester Briggs (her favourite photograph)*

the customers, continually eluding her grasp. But in spite of her constant association with the rich and the noble, Hester never lost the common touch, and I think that was an important factor in our friendship. As I have already remarked, Hester would gently reprove me when I became resentful about my mixed parentage. She herself was even more of a mixture than me, having several large black patches on her back to which she would playfully draw attention from time to time.

"Mother was white as snow," she used to tell me, "but Father was a real black devil. Always watch out for the black toms, Sylvia. They're the worst of the lot. Some people think they're lucky. Mother did. And look how she ended up. Me and five others due in a fortnight, not a fish-bone in the house and Father off on the spree with the little tabby next-door."

Yes, Hester had to work her way up from lowly beginnings. And all the benefits of her hard-won experience she freely showered on me. It was not long before I began to turn to her instead of to Mother for advice and help; and when Mother finally went out of my life, it seemed only natural that I should accept Hester's invitation to go and live with her in her cosy flat in Dolphin Square.

The last I was to see of Mother for some time to come was her posing for press cameras on the rail of the liner which took her to the United States, as the accompanying photograph from the *Daily Miaow* bears witness. The gentleman with her is Cyrus T. Rocksalmonfeller (in spite of his name, he was only

*The Kitty-Kat Club in its heyday*

half Persian, if that), owner of the vast Rocksalmon-feller Whiting Canneries in San Francisco. He and Mother had become great friends, and the idea was that I should follow her to San Francisco when she had established herself there. But I somehow knew it would be a long time before I would see Mother again. And when we did finally meet once more, how different were the circumstances from anything I could have imagined on that windy day at Southampton!

*The last I was to see of Mother for some time*

# CHAPTER III

## *Early days in the theatre*

L isten, my love," said Hester to me at supper one night a few weeks after Mother's departure, "I'm afraid we must start facing facts. Much as it pains me to tell you, I don't think we shall be hearing from your Mama for some time—if ever."

My heart sank. I was still cherishing the hope that one day soon I would follow Mother over the Atlantic and rejoin her in the Rocksalmonfeller Mansion in San Francisco. But Hester's words made me admit to myself that I had been building castles in the air. We had not even received a postcard to tell us of Mother's safe arrival, and as she had left no address, I realised I would have to resign myself to being, temporarily at any rate, an orphan.

"Now don't look so sad, ducky," went on Hester. "You've got me to look after you. All you've got to do now is to decide on a career. What about going on the stage?"

The stage! The idea appealed to me immediately. I knew next to nothing about the Theatre, my only personal contact with it being rather dim memories of some of Mother's friends. But I had been to several shows with Hester since she had taken me under her wing, and the bright lights and the glamour had made an indelible impression on my adolescent mind. I told Hester that I would love to be an actress, but had no idea how to go about it.

"Leave it to me," said Hester, resourceful as always. "I have contacts. Just drink up your milk and then off to bye-byes. We want you looking your best in the morning."

So it came about that a few weeks later I set off for my first class at Madame Alicia Whiskeronova's Academy of Drama and Dance in Notting Hill Gate. Madame Alicia was an old friend of Hester's, and she had agreed to take me on special terms, on Hester's assurance that I was extremely talented and would be a credit to Madame's Academy. Needless to say it was Hester who paid my fees, partly out of her savings and partly from the proceeds of a small gambling club which she had opened in her Dolphin Square flat on Wednesday and Saturday evenings. This I only discovered at a later date, as I was always sent off to bed early on these occasions, and was usually too exhausted after my day's classes to pay any attention to the noises that emanated from Hester's sitting-room. I believe that the police called one night, but discovered nothing, as Hester had things so carefully organised that it was a matter of minutes to dispose of the gambling apparatus and transform the gathering into what was, to all intents and purposes, a poetry-reading group, with Hester declaiming a passage from "Old Possum."

I have vivid recollections of my time with Madame Alicia and her sister, Madame Lydia, as indeed must many of our present-day stars who passed through their firm but loving hands. How strict Madame Alicia could be and how in awe of her we all were! Madame Lydia was gentler, but no less insistent on discipline at all times—one of the cardinal rules of the theatre. Their Academy was housed in an old drill hall which

*To all intents and purposes, a poetry-reading*

was only warmed in the winter by one unreliable oil stove; and there we would assemble, shivering with cold and nerves, for our dancing class at nine o'clock every morning. Unpunctuality was an unforgivable sin and I can remember the fearful tirade which Madame Alicia inflicted on one of my fellow-pupils, a pretty little tabby who had missed her train from Rickmansworth and arrived twenty minutes late. She was reduced to tears in no time, and her name was Lucy Trembath, who was destined to capture the heart of London when she sang "Just My Tom" in *Pussy, Be Good.*

I must confess that I was also a victim of Madame Alicia's displeasure from time to time. I am not by nature industrious—probably because of my aristocratic lineage—and I frequently found the long hours of instruction irksome. I was particularly backward in my ballet—in fact I never did learn to do an entrechat—and I was sometimes guilty of slacking, whenever I could evade Madame's watchful eye and find myself a place at the back of the class. Here I was usually joined by a black-and-white tom whose name was Sylvester. He showed even less aptitude for dancing than I did, and I remember his confiding in me that he intended becoming a comedian and going to Hollywood. Both these ambitions were of course realised, and I have to smile when I recall his rendering of Othello in our end-of-term show. His playing of the murder scene gave us a distinct foretaste of his great success as the would-be assassin of Tweety-Pie, the canary.

With Madame Lydia, who acted as the voice coach, my relations were a good deal more amicable. She told me early on in my course that my singing voice, if properly trained, while it would never be of operatic proportions, would serve me very well for musical comedy. I accordingly determined to make stardom on the lighter stage my goal, a decision to which Hester gave her full backing.

"That's the way to get a rich husband," she told me. "The drama is all very well, but you don't hear of straight actresses marrying into the peerage, now do you?"

As a matter of fact marriage, whether or not with a peer, was the last thing I had in mind at the time. I was altogether absorbed in my theatrical career, as were all Madame's pupils. Oh, what long sessions we would have over hot milk and fried fish in Joe Lion's Café at Notting Hill Gate, discussing shows and stars and airing our views about the Theatre! We

*How strict Madame Alicia could be!*

all had our favourites, whose careers we would follow with avidity. I remember Lucy Trembath, who fancied herself as a Shakespearean actress at the time, used to go in the gallery every Saturday night to watch Michael Redtail in *Hamlet* at the Mew Theatre. She always managed to get in the front row, and once nearly fell into the dress circle from excitement because, so she assured us, he waggled his whiskers at her during "Oh, what a rogue and peasant slave am I".

My own particular hero was Vincent Crabbe, who was then appearing in *The Dancing Toms*. I went to see the show countless times, sometimes with Hester, but more often on my own as I found a companion distracted me from my absorption in the performance. One night, in fear and trembling, I waited at the stage door to see Vincent Crabbe leaving the theatre. There

*Michael Redtail in "Hamlet"*

*He signed my programme "To Sylvia"*

was a crowd of fans there, and I only expected to have a brief glimpse of him. When he did finally emerge, he was immediately surrounded, and I hovered on the outskirts vainly hoping I might get near enough to ask him to sign my programme. To my surprise he noticed me and said laughingly, "Who is the little lady in grey?" I was quite overwhelmed and blushed to the roots of my fur. Then I summoned up my courage and told him my name. He was absolutely charming, and signed my programme "To Sylvia". I think it was at that moment that I decided that, whatever else I might do, my ultimate ambition would be to play the lead in a musical comedy opposite Vincent Crabbe.

Of course, like all students, we were usually short of funds, and to remedy this we would take on all sorts of odd jobs during our holidays. Modelling, whether for artists or photographers, was the most popular choice, and Lucy Trembath told me she was able to dress herself and pay her fares out of what she made posing for Christmas and birthday cards. But then of course she was and still is a typical picture-postcard cat. Another fellow-student, a handsome black tom, whose name I forget, made quite a reputation for himself as the mascot of a well-known brand of cigarette. In fact his publicity reached such proportions that Madame Alicia told him he must choose between learning to be an actor and being, as she contemptuously called it, a "pin-up tom".

On Hester's advice, I decided to try my luck as a fashion model. My figure had by this time the required proportions and my looks, so I flattered myself, had the necessary touch of breeding and ele-

*Lucy was a typical picture-postcard cat*

*I began by modelling hats for "Chatte"*

gance. I began by modelling hats for that well-known fashion magazine, *Chatte*, and was told that I could make a name for myself as a mannequin, if I chose. But my ambitions lay much higher, and although I was able to make quite a lot of "pin-money" in the photographer's studio, I only ever regarded modelling as a side-line. I don't believe it is generally known that I was the original Cuti-Cup Cat; in fact my first husband, on learning of it, endeavoured to suppress all the photographic evidence and even bought the original plates from the Cuti-Cup people and had them destroyed. But I managed to preserve one advertisement in an old scrap-book and have reproduced it here. I know that among certain circles that sort of thing is considered *infra dig.*, but I see no reason to conceal such amusing fragments of the past from my public.

When my time with Madame Alicia was nearing its end, Hester began to busy herself with securing me some sort of professional engagement.

"You must be prepared," she told me at the time,

"to start at the bottom. We all do it. But there's no reason why, with your looks and talent, you shouldn't work your way up to the top in no time at all."

I feel at this point that my readers may consider themselves cheated if I do not embark on a description of struggles and heartbreak—endless auditions, culminating in the customary "We'll let you know", jobs in the chorus of "tatty" touring musicals, or long weeks of repertory in some grim Northern town. The truth is, though I hesitate to admit it, that I was spared all this. Within a week or so of leaving Madame Whiskeronova's I was rehearsing as a dancer in a West End revue, *Tails Up!* Needless to say, I owed this "lucky break" mainly to Hester. For Emile Tiddler, who presented the show, had been a regular customer at the Kitty-Kat in the old days, and was only too glad to do Hester a favour by employing me. Naturally I was thrilled to bits to be working as a professional, and so was Lucy Trembath

*An amusing fragment of my past*

who was in the show with me, in the same dressing-room, and had managed to secure a "spot" in the show in the big "Pussy's Day-dreams" number, in which she was to do a toe-dance dressed as a jug of cream. She had quite got over her Shakespearean phase by now, and was, like myself, set upon a career on the musical stage. We were friendly rivals—although at the time more friends than rivals. In fact we collaborated in one or two rather disgraceful practical jokes during the run of the show, which nearly earned us our dismissal from Mr Tiddler. The one I remember most vividly was perpetrated while Lucy and I were waiting to go on for the chorus number in the second half, "Whose Kitten Are You?" The previous number was a song scena which took place in a gigantic bird-cage. Two of the show-cats were standing at the back dressed as birds of paradise and Lucy and I crept behind the scenery and with great care reached up and tied their tails together. When the scene ended they both began to dash offstage to make their next change (revue is so exhausting) and fell flat on their faces. Lucy and I were in paroxysms —how cruel the young can be!—and nearly missed our entrance. I don't believe the two show-cats ever found out who was responsible, and I shall take this opportunity of apologising to them at long last.

*Tails Up!* was moderately successful and ran for about six months. Towards the end of the run I read in *The Stage* that Vincent Crabbe was going to appear in another musical show in the autumn, for which auditions were being held at the Felix. I had always regarded that famous theatre, erected in honour of one of our greatest artists, as my Mecca, and I was a mass of nerves when I arrived, with hundreds of others, on the appointed morning, Hester's last words ringing in my ears: "Take a deep breath before you start, and use the *whole* stage." The Felix is of course one of the largest theatres in London, and the picture of myself attempting to use the whole of that vast stage was not an encouraging one. However, when my name was finally called, I tripped on with what was, I hope, an air of confidence, and after handing my music to the pianist launched into a verse and two choruses of "Whose Kitten Are You?", the second chorus being taken up with as elaborate a dance routine as Hester and I could devise. To my amazement, when I had finished, applause broke out in the stalls, and I heard a voice—Vincent Crabbe's voice—say from out of the darkness, "Thank you *very* much, Miss Sylvia". I know that one is accustomed to hear that at the end of even the worst audition; but there was something in his tone that made me feel that he meant it. I often wonder whether he recognised me as "the little lady in grey" to whom he had given his autograph. I don't suppose he did; but, what was more important, a day or two later I was informed that Mr Crabbe would like me to be in his show and I was to be one of the girls' octet in the first act.

Hester and I were beside ourselves with delight.

"This calls for a celebration, my pet," said Hester. "Come along. Get yourself dressed up and we'll go to Prunier's."

I protested about the expense; but Hester would have none of it.

"I've been doing rather well lately," she said—by this time I knew about the gambling club. "Some of the boys have been a bit reckless."

So off we went and had a wonderful evening. I ate my first lobster and adored it.

"That's right, love," said Hester. "It's time you developed expensive tastes." And I'm afraid I've followed her advice ever since.

We returned home at midnight, tired but happy, and a few days later I began rehearsing in my first show with Vincent Crabbe.

*Lucy managed*
*to secure a "spot"*

# CHAPTER IV

## *The bright lights*

Older theatregoers will not need to be reminded of the plot and setting of *The Princess and Me*, but, for the benefit of my younger readers, I would just like to say that it was a spectacular romantic musical set in Siam in the eighteenth century. Vincent Crabbe played an adventurer who arrives at the Siamese Court and falls in love with the princess, played by that wonderful Siamese star, Get Yû. The big scenes were the March of the Siamese Kittens and a ballet which was supposed to represent the untutored Siamese's idea of Puss in Boots, and was quite the most enchanting thing imaginable. My readers may wonder how I, a Persian (or almost a Persian), managed to acquire a part in a show set in Siam; but the reason was that the girls' octet represented the King of Siam's harem, which was naturally culled from all parts of the Orient. Lola Pickering, later to make her name in cabaret, was one of our number, and she of course is an Abyssinian. I believe I was actually supposed to be Circassian; but musical comedy has never been strictly accurate, and *The Princess and Me* was certainly no exception.

How I threw myself into rehearsals! Although I hardly spoke to Vincent Crabbe, except where a scene in the play required it, it was an inspiration to be working on the same stage, and I would come home in the evening to Dolphin Square in an exhausted daze. The weeks passed quickly, and before we knew where we were it was dress rehearsal, and then the opening night. Any first night is an event; but a Vincent Crabbe musical play at the Felix was something which all London awaited with breathless anticipation.

I was of course in a terrifying state of nerves which Hester did her best to alleviate. I received an amazing number of telegrams including several from the cast of *Tails Up* which had gone out on tour, my place having been taken by a very superior blue Persian girl, who, according to Lucy, was "no fun at all". Lucy's own telegram was typical of her: "Wow them all, darling! Whiskeronova's for ever!" She was in Huddersfield, poor thing, and very much missing the West End; but, as the curtain was about to go up on *The Princess and Me*, I had a wild desire to be back in the chorus with her, singing "Whose Kitten Are You?"

However, I need not have worried. From the moment Vincent Crabbe strode onto the stage, looking magnificent in navy blue and gold, the show was a wild success. And much to my delight, our octet in the first act, "Ladies of the Crown", had gone extremely well, and we had done an encore—in spite of the fact that Lola Pickering, unintentionally I'm sure, stepped on my tail just as I was reaching a high note and made me go sharp. She was profusely apologetic afterwards and I naturally forgave her, as my tail is unusually luxuriant and I am sometimes unaware myself of how far it extends.

The notices next day were unanimously enthusiastic—dividing their praise equally between the

show, Vincent Crabbe and Get Yû, who had looked
a dream in a succession of exquisite costumes and had
stopped the show with her waltz song at the end of the
first act. I was very thrilled to find that the octet had
not been overlooked either, and the *Daily Miaow* had
referred to us as "an assorted bevy of beauties". Hester
and I were so excited we went to Prunier's again—for
lunch—and this time I had crab. Over the meal we
made various rather elaborate plans about the future,
which included a trip abroad for Hester, who was beginning to feel her life at Dolphin Square was a little
confined.

"I might go to Famagusta again," she said, "just
for a month or so. I love the sunshine, you know,
dearie. This climate doesn't really suit me. My fur is
beginning to look definitely drab; a spell in Famagusta
would give me back a bit of a shine."

I was all for Hester's having a holiday. She had
been looking after me a long time, and now that I had
a good job to rely on, probably for months to come, it
seemed only right that she should have a rest. Also,
I must confess, I rather fancied being on my own in
London. Of course my work still came first; but I had
already acquired one or two admirers during the run
of *Tails Up!* and the success of *The Princess and Me*
would, I imagined, increase their number. Not that I
intended to take romance seriously for the moment;
but I was rapidly becoming conscious of my attraction
for the opposite sex, and, I suppose one might say,
vice versa.

After the excitement of the first night and the
press notices, *The Princess and Me* settled down to

*Get Yû looked a dream*

a long and successful run. On the whole I was thoroughly enjoying myself. There were several parties for the cast, and a good deal of publicity. In fact one day I received a postcard from Mother. There was no address on it—simply the words "Well done, darling. Your ever loving Mother", and on the other side a photograph of Reno; so we were really none the wiser, except for knowing that she was still in America. I wished she would come back to London to see her daughter performing on the stage, but she was obviously too involved in her life in America.

"It looks as if she's married again, ducky," said Hester. "Perhaps she's even had another family."

This wasn't a particularly encouraging thought, and I decided to forget about Mother for the time being. I certainly had other things to occupy my mind. Now that I was making some money I bought myself several new outfits and had my whiskers permed— which was considered very smart at the time. Hester said it aged me; but I was delighted.

My relationship with Vincent Crabbe was still the distant one of star and small-part player—in fact I saw much less of him now than during rehearsals— but he was very charming to all of us and gave the whole cast a magnificent party at his house in Finsbury Park on the night of our hundredth performance. It was rather a wild one, I remember—the first I had experienced—and Lola Pickering disgraced herself by falling into a bowl of cream. Everyone laughed at the time; but I don't think the management were too pleased about it, and there was a feeling of relief

*Lola Pickering disgraced herself*

when she left the show a few weeks later to play the lead in a revival of *The Quaker Cat* on tour. I must say that she and I, while not exactly "hitting it off", managed to avoid crossing swords; but there was always a slight atmosphere of unrest while she was in the company, and one of the stage managers, a very pleasant young ginger tom, in whom she had taken some interest, became so infatuated with her that one night he had to be forcibly restrained from lowering the curtain on Get Yû during her waltz song, because he felt Lola ought to have been singing it. The whole thing was of course hushed up at the time, but it was obvious that Lola was destined for a rather stormy career, and to those of us who knew her in *The Prin-*

*cess and Me* I don't believe the famous affair of the diamond engagement collar came as a great surprise.

The tour of *Tails Up!* finished in the New Year and I was very glad to see Lucy Trembath back in town again. She had somehow got herself engaged to a black-and-white business tom in Newcastle, "out of sheer boredom", so she told me. But she contrived to break it off within a few days of her return to London and was soon rehearsing for another revue, an intimate one this time, at the tiny Mousetrap Theatre off the Strand. "There's no money, and conditions are Hell," she told me, "but it is fun." I must say that I, beginning to experience the *ennui* of a long run, felt rather envious of her starting on something so novel. But when I finally saw the show, on a Sunday night, I realised that the small theatre was not my milieu. The audience was strange, to say the least of it, and the show, to quote Hester, who saw it with me, was "too clever by half". But Lucy came out of it very well, and was particularly amusing in a skit on *The Princess and Me*, which would probably have upset Get Yû but of which I was able to see the funny side.

*The audience was strange, to say the least of it*

And I'm glad to say that her appearance at the Mouse-trap Theatre proved to be the stepping-stone to Lucy's career as a musical-comedy star, for a producer saw her there and cast her in *Pussy, Be Good*, the show that made her name.

Meanwhile the months wore on, and the popularity of *The Princess and Me* showed no sign of flagging. In July Hester went off for her holiday in Famagusta and I received numerous tantalising picture postcards from her. On one of them she said, "The old place still looks the same, but the people are different. My fish restaurant is now a milk bar with a juke box. Can you imagine it?" However, she seemed to be enjoying herself and came back at the end of August looking very fit, her white fur tanned to an interesting beige. I found I missed her dreadfully, and being on my own in London in the hot summer months proved to be almost no fun at all. The place seemed to be quite empty except for tourist cats, who came to see the show of course, but were not the sort of people one would get to know. In fact I began to wish I were not in the theatre and tied to a long run but were instead a member of Society who could pack up and go abroad at the end of the season—ungrateful of me, I know, but quite natural in view of my ancestry.

But one night in September all this was changed with startling suddenness, and something happened which took even Hester by surprise.

Our star, Get Yû, had for some weeks been making a film during the day as well as performing in *The Princess and Me* at night. I know that West End stars often do this, and suffer no ill effects; but Siamese are naturally delicate, and Get Yû's role was particularly exhausting, as the film, whose title I'm afraid I forget, was one of those Oriental adventure stories which involved the heroine in all sorts of strenuous escapades, most of which she had to perform wearing the same sort of elaborate costumes as she did in *The Princess and Me*. We had noticed that on some evenings she appeared to show signs of strain. I remember that one night she left out the top G in the waltz song completely. Of course, the audience never noticed—it's surprising what audiences miss—but the rest of the cast did. However, we were not unduly worried as theatre people have a firm faith in that famous slogan, "The Show Must Go On", and don't usually anticipate trouble until it is actually upon them.

So on the night I have already referred to, the night which was to affect my life so unexpectedly, the curtain rose as usual on the opening scene, with all of us singing away quite unconcernedly in the first number, "Sweet Siam". Vincent Crabbe made his entrance and received the usual round of applause. Then came the moment when the Princess is announced. This was built up very elaborately by music and singing and culminated in the entire cast turning upstage with one paw out while Vincent Crabbe remained downstage left looking suitably eager. But this time nothing happened. We all stood there paralysed, none of us knowing what to do. Then suddenly, to my horror, I realised what had gone wrong. My position was right upstage, behind all the others, so that I was able to see into the wings, and there, hidden from view by a piece of scenery, I caught sight of poor Get Yû. She had collapsed in a dead faint just as she was about to go on, and none of the stage staff had seen her. What was I to do? The musical director, sensing what had happened, was launching into a repeat of the entrance music, while the cast were still holding up their paws—though rather shakily by now. In a flash I made up my mind: I must save the situation! While the entrance music crashed into its final bars, I slipped into the wings, exchanged my own head-dress for Get Yû's and, bracing myself, walked slowly onstage again.

What followed has, I'm afraid, melted into a strange haze in which I remember the hastily concealed looks of astonishment of the rest of the cast, the uncertain applause of the audience, who must have been baffled by Get Yû's sudden transformation into a Persian, and myself singing and speaking as if in a trance, wondering whether I would remember the next line or move and finding myself doing them automatically.

The scene luckily was a short one and I scarcely had time to realise the responsibility I had undertaken. Vincent Crabbe, once he had got over the understandable shock of suddenly being confronted with a new leading lady, played up to me beautifully. I made my exit, this time to whole-hearted applause, and nearly fainted in the arms of the stage manager, who had by now realised what was wrong and called the understudy. I handed over Get-Yû's head-dress and staggered up to my dressing-room. A few moments later Vincent Crabbe rushed in and, to my delight and amazement, kissed me warmly on both cheeks. I had been terrified that he would be annoyed; instead he was full of praise for my resourcefulness.

"You, my dear Sylvia," he exclaimed, "are now a star!"

The rest of the cast were equally flattering and I went through the remainder of the performance, once more in my usual role, lost in a haze of happiness. It was only when I finally came home and told Hester of the night's events that I realised I had achieved my ambition: I had played opposite Vincent Crabbe.

The papers next day all carried a story about me. "Chorus girl takes over from leading lady", the headlines said, and before long the 'phone was ringing and reporters came to interview me. A special messenger brought a large bouquet of cat-mint from Vincent Crabbe, and Get Yû sent a message of thanks from the nursing home where she had been taken by ambulance the night before. What a day it was! Contracts were dangled in front of me by agents and managers—none of which I signed, thanks to Hester —and our little flat was transformed into a bedlam.

During the weeks that followed, I gradually became aware that I had achieved fame at last. I continued to play my part in *The Princess and Me*, but the management had decided to bring the run to an end, as Get Yû had been ordered to take a rest cure and although the understudy was very good, the business began to drop and no other Siamese star was available to take over the part. After my initial publicity had died down, Hester and I set about de-

*Laurence Fortescue*

ciding which of the many offers I had received was
the one to accept. The most tempting was the leading
role in Laurence Fortescue's new operetta, which he
had just completed while on holiday in the Bahamas.
He came to see me at the Felix one night—apparently
on the recommendation of Vincent Crabbe—and I
immediately fell under the spell of his well-known
charm. He explained that he was looking for someone
new and unknown to play the part of an Edwardian
songstress who has a tragic love affair with a Ruri-
tanian prince. He was going to call the show *That
Old Fragrance* and the whole thing sounded quite
enchanting.

I began rehearsals shortly after *The Princess and Me* had closed, and, although I started off with serious misgivings about my ability to undertake a leading role, I soon gained confidence, thanks to Laurence's expert and sympathetic direction. He was a delight to work with, and all the cast adored him. I know that nowadays he is considered somewhat of a period piece, but at the time I knew him he was at the height of his powers, and I think it is generally agreed that his music and lyrics for *That Old Fragrance* were among the best he ever wrote. My waltz song in the Ascot

*"That Old Fragrance"*

scene, "This is Good-bye", has since become a classic of its kind, and of course everyone remembers the brilliant Society Hostesses' quartet which kept recurring throughout the show. My favourite verse was:

> *My daughter, Harriet,*
> *Is eager to wed.*
> *It's a shame about her dreadful teeth,*
> *But she has a heart of gold beneath,*
> *And I'm sure the Marquis of Blackheath*
> *Wouldn't notice them in bed.*
> *Oh, Society hostesses*
> *Lead such a worrying life,*
> *Looking for a nobleman*
> *Who is looking for a wife.*

What wit and polish! I know that nowadays the American musical shows are all the rage, but to me they seem slightly brash compared with a Fortescue operetta, and I think there are a good many theatre-goers of my generation who would agree with me.

The costumes for *That Old Fragrance* were of course designed by Edwina Lessiter, who did the décor for all the Fortescue shows, and how pretty they were! How I wish I could reproduce the accompanying photo of myself in colour! My dress was the most delicate shade of salmon pink—very flattering to my grey fur —decorated with blue and mauve embroidery, and I believe the whole effect was quite breathtaking.

Well, as everyone knows, *That Old Fragrance* was an enormous success. The first night was unforgettable. Hester was there, of course, in a gold lamé

*The stage box*

frock she had bought in Paris on her way back from Famagusta. And there in the stage box was Laurence Fortescue, with, of course, dear old Mrs Fortescue (to whom he always said he owed everything), Edwina Lessiter, his manager, Geoffrey Whitebait, and his secretary, Madge—all of whom had been with him for years. After the cast had taken innumerable curtain calls, Laurence came on to the stage and made a most amusing and touching little speech. And then, with such a gallant gesture, he turned and led me forward. The applause was deafening, and, I regret to say, I burst into tears. What a moment! I could see Hester, standing on her seat in the stalls, cheering, and I realised with an indescribable thrill that I was a star!

# CHAPTER V

## *First love*

Stardom brought in its train several changes in my hitherto rather unsensational existence. In the first place I set up house on my own. I was naturally reluctant to leave Hester's cosy flat, where I had been so happy and well looked after; but as she herself said to me, "You're a big cat now, dearie, and it's time you started living a life of your own." So one day a week or so after *That Old Fragrance* had opened, we went house-hunting together, and after an arduous search we discovered a sweet little maisonette in a mews in Belgravia. I had always wanted to live in a mews, and the day I moved in I felt that I had really attained the height of my ambition. I told Hester this, but she only smiled mysteriously and said, "You won't be here long, my girl: no one as pretty as you is going to live on her own for ever."

In actual fact she was, as usual, right. But I had a very happy time in my new little house during the run of *That Old Fragrance* and did a lot of entertaining. In fact before long my Sunday afternoon cream parties became quite fashionable among the élite of the theatre world, and Laurence Fortescue, Vincent Crabbe and Lucy Trembath attended them regularly, as did several other stars of the time. Lucy was now engaged to a wealthy gentleman farmer from Catterick, who seemed very devoted to her; but *Pussy, Be Good* had just opened and she was on the threshold of a brilliant career in the theatre. So I was not surprised when she rang me up one morning and told me the engagement was off. She had now moved into town from Rickmansworth to a flat not far from my mews, so we saw a great deal of each other and often had long sessions over a dish of milk, reminiscing about our days at Whiskeronova's and our exploits in the chorus of *Tails Up!* Occasionally Lucy would ask me if I intended to get married, and I always said, "No, not just yet", as I still felt that my career came first. Of course I had several admirers, some of whom I was sincerely fond of: but that is nothing unusual once one has become a star, and, although they would propose to me from time to time, I never took any of them seriously. In any case I was still far too much in love with my new-found freedom to entertain the prospect of having a family of kittens. Hester would drop hints from time to time about the advisability of making a good marriage—in fact she went so far as to introduce me to a number of eligible young Society toms, most of them sons of former members of the Kitty-Kat Club—but I usually changed the subject of conversation, and after a time she gave it up as a bad job.

*That Old Fragrance* ran for over a year in London, and then we were told that it had been decided to take the show over to New York. At first I was not too keen to go. I had just completed the final touches to my new house and established for myself a circle of congenial and intelligent friends. New York seemed a long way away, and in any case I was mildly allergic to American cats—perhaps because of a childhood resentment against Cyrus T. Rocksalmonfeller who had taken my mother away from me (or so I had imagined at the time). However, as soon as I told Hester about it, she was delighted and pooh-poohed any suggestion of my leaving the cast of the show.

"It's the land of opportunity, my love," she said. "I went there once in the old days, and, believe me, I had opportunities all the time. American toms take a bit of getting used to—they're not as reliable as English boys—but they'll give you a wonderful time, Sylvia. You go, my sweet, you won't regret it."

It had also occurred to me that, if I went to the United States, I might re-establish contact with my mother. I had received another postcard after the opening of *That Old Fragrance*, this time with a picture of Las Vegas. But the message was the same as before and gave no clue as to where Mother was living or what she might be doing. So I finally decided to go to New York with the show. I let the mews house to Lucy, who was tired of her flat, and after a tearful farewell to Hester at Southampton I set sail.

Looking back on my first visit to New York, I always feel that it is not so much a place as an experience. Many other more talented writers than myself have described it, so I shall not take up my readers' time with my own attempt to do so. From the moment we stepped on shore—Laurence Fortescue (with Edwina, Geoffrey, Madge and old Mrs Fortescue), myself and the other stars of the show—we were made welcome in the most enthusiastic manner. There were parties every night, visits to shows (the best, as far as I remember, being *Kiss Me, Cat*) and press receptions, none of which I seemed to find tiring, owing to

New York's electric atmosphere, which one can feel tingling in one's whiskers. The show finally opened, and, when the notices came out, the round of hospitality ceased abruptly, for they were, I regret to say, rather tepid. However, fortunately for me, the critics liked my performance, and the *New York Caterwaul* actually went so far as to say I was "the best import from Britain since Scotch haddock"—rather a farfetched compliment, but gratifying none the less. Laurence Fortescue took the failure of the show quite calmly and departed with his entourage on the next boat to the Bahamas; but the cast were heart-broken and set about booking their return trips to England. I was about to do the same, when I received a call from the Goldfisch Studios in Hollywood. I had never thought of myself as a film actress till that moment; but when I was asked to play the part of an English girl in a "crazy comedy" called *The Cat's Pyjamas*, I decided I had nothing to lose by accepting. I would at least return to London with some money in my pocket, and I had always wanted to see what Hollywood was really like. I accordingly sent a cable to Hester telling her what had happened, and boarded a 'plane for California.

Little did I know, as I sped over the American continent, that my life was about to enter a new and totally different phase. I had every intention of completing my role in the film and returning to London and my Belgravia mews. But Fate decreed otherwise and much more than I could possibly imagine was destined to happen to me before I once more set paw on English soil.

*Nelly Nipper*

However, I am anticipating. My reception in Hollywood was, if anything, more tumultuous than the one we had received in New York. Visiting English actresses were more of a rarity than they are nowadays, and everyone seemed anxious to meet me. They were particularly fascinated by my family background and I was subjected to a long and detailed cross-examination about my aristocratic forbears by Nelly Nipper, who was then, as I believe she still is, one of the leading Hollywood "gossip columnists". Somewhat against my will, as I did not really wish the fact to be publicised, I told her about Mother's disappearance to America during my early adolescence, and, to my horror, the story was featured in the papers the next day. The headlines said "English star comes to Hollywood to search for long-lost mother" or something to that effect, and, although I had no wish to broadcast the vagaries of my upbringing, the Goldfisch Studios were delighted, as, so they told me, the American public is exceedingly mother-conscious, and such a story would appeal to them immensely. They decided to institute a nation-wide search for Mother, and as I was naturally anxious to see her again, I raised no objection.

In the meanwhile, I set about preparing myself for my first film role. Screen acting had formed no part of the Whiskeronova curriculum—in fact Madame Alicia had rather frowned on it—so I began my first day's shooting with all the nervousness of a complete novice. But I need not have worried, as I found I merely had to do exactly what the director told me. Everyone seemed very satisfied with my "rushes", and from then on I took to filming with the greatest of ease. My part was not a rewarding one—a conventional English ingénue, who somehow became involved in the more sophisticated goings-on of the stars, Barbara Bream and Red Flounder—but I photographed very well and wore some pretty clothes, so I was quite satisfied.

One morning during the second week of shooting Mr Goldfisch himself suddenly appeared on the set, followed by several attendants carrying bottles of champagne, and a small band of reporters and press photographers, and ordered work to stop. We were all quite mystified for a moment, and then a door opened at the other end of the studio, and in walked Nelly Nipper with someone whom I recognised with difficulty as being Mother! She had been found at last! I felt myself go weak at the knees, but Mr Goldfisch took my arm and led me towards her, and at the same time the flashlights began to pop. Mother and I fell into each other's arms, and I had just time to hear her say "If this doesn't make a star of you, nothing will", before glasses of champagne were thrust into our hands and the reporters began bombarding us with questions.

I'm afraid it was only a brief reunion. It transpired that Mother had read the story about me in the newspaper in her hotel in Reno, where she was in the middle of her third divorce. She had waited until the decree was made final and then taken the next 'plane to Hollywood. "It was more or less on my way, dear," she whispered to me. "You see, my next husband is waiting for me in Honolulu."

We were given a grand lunch by Mr Goldfisch, at the end of which everyone, including Mother and myself, made speeches. I could see she wasn't enjoying it very much and kept looking at the time.

*My brief reunion with Mother*

*"Salome"*

"If I miss that 'plane, Louie will be furious," she said to me in an aside. "He's got the most divine plantation, right on the seashore. Just imagine, fresh fish every day, straight out of the Pacific! I'll send you a picture postcard."

I tried to make Mother stay with me for a day or two in Hollywood, but she insisted on leaving as soon as lunch was finished, with only a vague promise that she would visit me when her new honeymoon was over.

"You've got a career, darling," were her last words, "and so, in a way, have I. Unfortunately family life has to be sacrificed."

*"Anna Catrenina"*

So I kissed her goodbye and returned to the set feeling rather forlorn but also reluctantly convinced that she was right.

As Mother foresaw, the publicity resulting from our reunion did make a star of me in Hollywood. Mr Goldfisch offered me a long-term contract, which, after a conversation over the 'phone with Hester, I decided to accept. She promised to come out and visit me soon and said that she would look after my affairs in London. I couldn't help feeling a pang of nostalgia when I realised it might be years before I saw my native country again; but, owing to my haphazard upbringing, my roots had never been deep, and I soon found

*"An Alley-cat named Désirée"*

that the Californian climate and life in Hollywood suited me very well.

When my part in *The Cat's Pyjamas* ended, I was rushed straight into the lead in the film version of *Kiss Me, Cat,* as someone had remembered that I could sing. A variety of roles followed, too numerous to mention individually; but I have included a selection of "stills" from my more successful films, just to remind my readers of the highlights of my Hollywood career.

I must say at this point that, although film stardom may appear to have come to me the easy way, it brought with it several handicaps, not the least of which was the jealousy of other actresses. The one who most resented my sudden rise to fame was the

*"The Goldfisch Follies"*

leading star in the Goldfisch Studios, Miaow-Miaow Latouche. She, as my readers will doubtless remember, was a cat of great beauty, but not, in my humble opinion, blessed with remarkable histrionic talent. Her background was unusually obscure, as her mother was supposed to be an aristocrat of vaguely mid-European extraction, who had arrived in America as a refugee, bringing with her a family of girl kittens, all of whom had grown up to be great beauties and had then proceeded to form liaisons of various natures with leading American politicians, financiers and film stars. Miaow-Miaow herself had been married three times, to say nothing of less legal but equally publicised associations, and was currently reported to be in the middle of a hectic love affair with a millionaire oil magnate, Blackie Diabolo. He was, I suppose, the most eligible bachelor in Hollywood at the time, and Nelly Nipper was continually predicting whom he would marry, usually on the flimsiest evidence.

I first met Blackie at the première of Miaow-Miaow's latest film, *Salmon for Breakfast*. These premières were enormous affairs, and Mr Goldfisch liked all his stars to attend them, looking their best. I happened to arrive just after Miaow-Miaow, and while she was surrounded by reporters and photographers, I found myself standing next to an extremely handsome black cat, who was, of course, Mr Diabolo. He offered me a cigarette, and the next thing I knew a flash bulb exploded in our faces. I thought nothing of it at the time; but the next morning, to my horror, I found that the picture was in the paper over a typical piece of Nelly Nipper's gossip, headlined, "Look out,

Miaow-Miaow! Sylvia's moving in!" I was naturally a little annoyed, but decided to treat the whole thing as a joke. Miaow-Miaow, on the other hand, was furious, and, so I heard later, went straight to Mr Goldfisch's office and made a dreadful scene. Of course this was simply playing into Nelly Nipper's paws, and her story was further confirmed by the arrival on the set where I was working that morning, of a huge bouquet of Cattleya containing a card, on which was written: "We're dining to-night. Blackie". I was completely bewildered and had no idea what to do. However, I wasn't given much chance to make up my own mind. That evening a large car drew up at my front door (I had moved to a small villa in Beverly Hills) and inside it was Blackie with another bouquet. Before I could protest, I was in the car and being driven off in the direction of the Lobster Pot, Hollywood's favourite rendezvous at the time. What an evening it

*Miaow-Miaow (after an incident at the Lobster Pot)*

was! Cream flowed like water, I danced with Blackie until my legs ached, and throughout it all the flash bulbs kept exploding. I realised that I had now committed myself to being Blackie's latest "romance." I kept wondering what Miaow-Miaow would do, and at one moment I tried to ask Blackie about her. But he brushed my question aside with a laugh.

"Don't worry about her," he said gaily. "She has plenty of other fish to fry."

So Blackie and I continued to see each other nearly every evening, and gifts of flowers and jewellery kept arriving at my Beverly Hills villa. All this was, of course, eagerly reported by Nelly Nipper, which only served to increase Miaow-Miaow's fury. She stormed off the set one morning and refused to go on working unless I was sacked, for which Mr Goldfisch suspended her. And then one evening we came face to face at the Lobster Pot. I was terrified, as Miaow-Miaow had been known to assault her rivals, and everyone in the room had stopped eating in anticipation of a scene. I think there would have been one too, if Blackie had not intervened, for, as soon as she saw me, Miaow-Miaow grabbed a large sole from a plate on a nearby table. She was obviously about to slap me with it, but Blackie stepped between us and said in his most charming manner, "Lay off it, Miaow-Miaow. This isn't the Rue de Lappe." I'm not quite sure what he meant but it seemed to strike home, and with that he took my arm and led me out of the restaurant.

I think it was that evening that I realised I was in love with Blackie. In love for the first time in my life

*Blackie and I in the South of France*

—but under what unusual circumstances! I had no idea whether my feelings were reciprocated, and I remembered with sickening clarity Hester's oft-repeated warning about black cats. I suddenly felt I needed her desperately, so I rang her up the next morning, and within a few days she had arrived in Hollywood, looking just the same. I told her my dilemma, and, as usual, she rose to the occasion.

"Run away, love," she advised me without hesitation. "If he follows you, you'll know it's the real thing. If he doesn't—well, you need a holiday anyway."

That was certainly true, and luckily I was in between films, having just completed my role in *Cat's*

*Cradle*, a mother-love drama. So when I asked Mr Goldfisch for leave of absence from the studios, he was quite agreeable, and within a few hours Hester and I had set off for Europe. I did not even leave a message for Blackie to say I was going; in fact I made up my mind to forget him.

Hester decided we should make for the South of France, and we arrived in Nice in due course, thoroughly exhausted both by the trip and the effort to evade reporters. I was officially travelling incognito, but it seemed impossible to keep my real identity a secret (I was quite a favourite on the Continent) and Hester was hard put to it to protect me from the prying eye of the Press. However, once installed in a small and inconspicuous hotel in Nice, we felt safer, and both of us took a long and sorely needed rest.

But my respite from publicity was destined to be short-lived. After a few days spent sun-bathing and taking car rides along the Côte d'Azur (it was my first visit), I was woken one morning by the telephone ringing by my bed. It was the hotel manager to tell me that I had a visitor. I hardly needed him to inform me who it was, and, sure enough, a few moments later, Blackie was in my room. We were together again!

This time our romance was more in earnest. After a day or two in Nice, during which reporters followed us everywhere, we decided to make a dash for it. The plan was that Blackie should go to Paris and I should go to Rome, to give the Press the idea that we had quarrelled. After a suitable interval we would both make our way, incognito if possible, to Budapest. Needless to say, our plans misfired and we were greeted in Budapest by a battery of news-cameras. So we turned round and took the next 'plane for Athens. What a whirlwind affair! In a matter of weeks we had covered most of Europe, and our romance was head-line news. Meanwhile the Studios were becoming anxious, partly because they felt my publicity was a little at variance with the sort of role I usually played (my next film was due to be *Joan of Arc*), and also because my prolonged absence from Hollywood was costing them a great deal of money.

It was in Venice that my first romance came to a sudden and disastrous end. Early one morning the police broke into our hotel bedroom and arrested Blackie. It seemed that Miaow-Miaow Latouche was determined to get her revenge. She had sponsored an investigation into Blackie's past, which had brought to light several disagreeable but undeniable facts. To my distress it turned out that he already had a wife and six kittens in Puerto Rico; and, as if this were not enough, the halibut oil well in New Mexico, in which he had sold several million dollars' worth of shares,

turned out to be non-existent. But I need not go into the details of a case which became headline news for several days in all the newspapers of the world. All that concerned me was that my first love affair had reached an untimely conclusion, and there was I alone in Venice, a sadder but a wiser cat.

# CHAPTER VI

## *A new life*

When I had recovered from the shock of
Blackie's arrest, my first impulse was, as
usual, to send for Hester. Also as usual, she
came by the first available 'plane, and, under her
ministrations, I soon began to feel much better about
the whole thing. I must give Hester credit for never at
any time reproaching me over the Blackie Diabolo
affair, in spite of the fact that she had warned me to
beware of black toms. She told me later that she had
fully expected the romance to come to an end before
long, although not in quite the way it actually happened; but she had done nothing to interfere, because
she felt that it was what I needed at that stage in my
life to make me into a completely adult cat. She was
certainly right.

"And now, dearie," she said, after she had been
with me a few days, and I was beginning to take an
interest in life again, "you've got to decide what you're
going to do. I suggest you take the next 'plane back to
America and get down to work again. I'm sure the
Goldfisch Studios will welcome you back, and playing
Joan of Arc will be just the thing to make you forget
what's happened."

I couldn't entirely agree with her over this. In fact
I very much doubted if Mr Goldfisch would counte-
nance my appearing as the Maid of Orleans after my
participation in what, as far as the general public was
concerned, could only be described as a rather lurid
romance. My doubts were confirmed a day or two later

by the announcement that the part had been given to
Miaow-Miaow Latouche—a hardly less unsuitable
piece of casting, in my opinion; but, as everyone
knows, the film was a disastrous flop. In any case, as I
explained to Hester, I felt that for me Hollywood was
now a closed chapter. Since leaving there I had become
too deeply embroiled in reality to return to a world of
make-believe.

In fact, after a serious discussion with Hester and
a few hours' solitary meditation while drifting round

*A few hours' solitary meditation*

Venice in a gondola, I decided that my career as an
actress was over. I had fulfilled all my ambitions and
given as much of myself to the Public as they could
reasonably expect. Besides, much as I enjoyed the
glamour and excitement of life "on the boards", I had
never at heart been a real "pro". As I have mentioned
before, I am not by nature industrious, and, as some of

my readers will know, the bright lights of the Theatre
are merely a façade to conceal an extremely hardwork-
ing existence.

Of course I was at the time receiving numerous
offers of films and plays from studios and manage-
ments eager to "cash in" on the publicity I had been
given over my association with Blackie. I also had
a letter from Vincent Crabbe asking me to play
opposite him in a new revival of one of his greatest
successes, *The Maid of the Miaowntains*. This was a
part I had always wanted to play, and under other
circumstances I would have accepted with alacrity.
But I turned it down along with all the others, in
spite of Hester's protests. I had decided that I would
go into retreat from the world and from the life I
had known, and when I informed Hester of this, she
had, as usual, no difficulty in arranging it for me.

"I know just the place, my pet," she told me, "and
funnily enough it's right here in Italy—just outside
Florence. As a matter of fact I could do with a little bit
of a retreat myself so I'll come there with you, unless
you've got any objection."

Of course I was only too delighted, and Hester set
about making arrangements. It turned out that one
of her friends in the Kitty-Kat days had been Vera
Smythe-Haddock, who had been a leading light of
the Bright Young Cats and was well known for her
impromptu saxophone solos in the night clubs of London and Paris. She used to appear regularly at the
Kitty-Kat Club and accompany Hester while she sang
"Milk for Two" from *Miaow, Miaow, Mabel* and of
course she had also known Mother quite well. How-

ever, when the Slump came she had abandoned her life of gaiety and turned to religion. She ceased to communicate with any of her friends, and finally took the veil. Quite by chance, through a mutual acquaintance who was visiting Florence, Hester had heard that she was now Mother Superior of the nunnery of Santa Caterina, which is situated on a hill a little way out of the city, in the most delightful surroundings. And it was there that she suggested we should go into retreat.

We accordingly left Venice a few days later, both of us heavily veiled so as not to be recognised by the reporters who were still hanging round our hotel. When we arrived at Santa Caterina, worn out by a hot and dusty journey, we were cordially welcomed by Vera Smythe-Haddock, an imposing figure in her nun's habit, and shown to a simply furnished double

*Vera Smythe-Haddock in the old days*

cell with an excellent view of Florence. How peaceful and serene it all seemed after my hectic existence of the last few months! It was exactly what I required to help me adjust myself and reorientate my life. I had plenty of time during the ensuing weeks to review the past and plan for the future, and Vera, with her fund of experiences and her wide knowledge of matters both sacred and profane, was an ideal adviser. At one point I was almost persuaded to follow her example and take the veil. The life of a nunnery seemed such a delightful contrast to the frenzied rush of Hollywood, and, what is more, the habit suited me, as I discovered when Hester and I tried it on one day just to see how it would look. But on the other hand, I had a strong premonition that my worldly existence was far from being over and that, if I were to retire from it permanently at this stage, I would live to regret it. Hester was of course very much against the scheme from the start.

"If you do it, love," she said to me, "then I shall have to too, and I honestly don't feel I'm cut out to be a nun."

However, I was still in a state of indecision about the whole matter, when Fate once more stepped in and made up my mind for me.

Hester, not surprisingly, had not taken to the seclusion of Santa Caterina quite as readily as I had—she had, after all, nothing in particular to escape from and had only accompanied me there out of the goodness of her heart. So, when we had been there a few weeks and Vera Smythe-Haddock suggested we might like

*The habit suited me*

to go with her on one of her errands of mercy to the slums of Florence, Hester welcomed the opportunity of a glimpse of the world outside the nunnery walls, and I could see no harm in going too. The Diabolo affair was no longer being featured in the press and we had successfully covered up our tracks on leaving Venice, so that there was little chance of my being recognised, especially in the rather plain and sombre outfit which I had decided was suitable for nunnery wear.

So the next morning found us in the streets of Florence, with their gay shops and busy cafés, and I must confess that this sight of the civilisation on which I had just recently turned my back did not fill me with the revulsion I had half expected to feel. In fact, when Vera suggested that Hester and I might like to stay on in town for lunch, while she returned to Santa Caterina, I raised no objection. The nunnery fare, while well-cooked, was extremely simple and tended to be repetitious, so that when Hester led me off to one of Florence's best restaurants, I was almost as excited as I had been on the occasion of our first visit to Prunier's—how long ago that seemed!

We were just going in, when Hester stopped short with an exclamation of surprise.

"Look!" she cried, "there's Miriam Boot!"

I followed her gaze and saw coming down the street a rather unusual figure—a large tabby wearing a yachting blazer and a slightly battered Panama hat. I had of course heard of Miriam Boot, as who has not? She too had made her name in the days of the Kitty-Kat Club and the Bright Young Cats. Her first novel, *Fish-heads*, had caused a sensation, won several awards and been banned in one or two countries. Since then she had built up a solid literary reputation with her down-to-earth stories of life and love in the slums of the great cities or the farming communities of the English countryside. I had dipped into some of her novels; but I am not a great reader at the best of times, and on the odd occasion when I feel like going to bed with a book, I usually choose something a little lighter than Miriam Boot.

She recognised Hester at once and, after I had been introduced, she suggested we should all have lunch together. Over the meal we told her our reason for being in Florence, and she was very intrigued to hear about me and Blackie.

"Make a good novel," she said, in her gruff way. "But I couldn't write it. Never touch that sort of stuff. More the type of thing you get in Lalage de Furrier."

When we told her about Santa Caterina, she was rather dumbfounded.

"Fancy old Vera being there," she said. "Never knew it and I've had a villa here for five years now. We must all get together and have a good old chinwag over old times. Do you remember Vera and Ronnie Kipperthwaite landing on the Albert Memorial by parachute? Had to call the fire brigade to get 'em down. They'd meant to land in Hyde Park, but they'd miscalculated the wind direction."

She and Hester were soon launched on a flood of reminiscence, and when we rose to go about two hours later, Miriam suggested that we move into her villa.

"Nunneries are all right, if you like that sort of thing," she said, "but Sylvia's too young to shut herself up with a lot of females. Come to my villa. You can do what you like, as long as you don't disturb me. Working on the tenth volume of my autobiography."

I was a little hesitant about accepting her invitation

but Hester was obviously keen to leave Santa Caterina although she did her best to hide it. So it was finally arranged that we should move over to Miriam's a few days later, for an indefinite stay.

I could not help feeling a pang of regret when we left the quiet confines of Santa Caterina, although Vera Smythe-Haddock had assured me that I would be welcomed back at any time I felt in need of a respite from the trials and tribulations of the outside world. I wondered if I was really ready to cope with Life again—Life that had brought me such glittering prizes and then dealt me such bitter blows. However, I comforted myself with the thought that at least the world of Miriam Boot was very different from the one I had left behind me at the end of my affair with Blackie.

The first few days of our stay at the Villa Tomboli were quiet and uneventful. We saw little of Miriam, who spent most of the day, and sometimes the evenings as well, closeted in a gazebo at the bottom of the garden, working on her autobiography. Apart from the Italian servants, our only other companion was Edith, Miriam's secretary, a faded tortoise-shell of uncertain age who had been with her for many years. She was obviously devoted to Miriam, who bullied her unmercifully. We would often hear Miriam shouting at her inside the gazebo, and once Edith appeared at dinner with her eyes red from weeping. She was by nature very reticent, but I managed to get into conversation with her later in the evening, and it transpired that Miriam had thrown a typewriter at her that afternoon—which had luckily missed—because she had discovered a comma missing from Edith's typescript. This set me wondering if the literary world might not turn out to be just as tempestuous as the world of the cinema.

Our leisurely existence was further interrupted a few days later by the arrival of Pandora Tickell and her brother, Lucian. They had been in Rome working on a script for the film version of Dante's Inferno. The whole project was being sponsored by the Goldfisch Studios and had degenerated into such a state of chaos that the Tickells had decided to retreat to Florence and throw themselves on Miriam's hospitality. Apparently, Mr Goldfisch was insisting that Beatrice should be written into the story to provide a star part for Barbara Bream, who, my readers may remember, was in my first Hollywood film. Naturally the Tickells considered this an outrage on their literary integrity and had threatened to withdraw from the whole business.

I found Pandora Tickell a most unusual person. Her taste in clothes was quite bizarre and she would wander round the villa and its gardens looking like an evocation of the Italian Renaissance. We had several long and stimulating conversations, and she was particularly interested in my Hollywood experiences and my romance with Blackie. At first I was rather reluctant to discuss such matters with a complete stranger, but I soon found myself responding to her eager questions. She was especially intrigued by Miaow-Miaow Latouche, whom she had met briefly at a literary luncheon in London, when Miaow-Miaow was involved in her short-lived affair with a novelist of in-

*Edith was obviously devoted to Miriam*

ternational renown. Pandora kept referring to her as
"The Modern Lilith"—a nickname whose significance
was rather beyond me, but it seemed to amuse Miriam
Boot.

With the advent of the Tickells, Miriam began
to devote less time to her autobiography and more to
entertaining her guests. There would be lengthy literary discussions in the evenings after dinner, in which
neither Hester nor I were able to join, but which were
none the less amusing to listen to. From time to time
Pandora Tickell would rise and declaim passages from
her new cycle of poems, "The Chaffinch and the Cod",
most of which I'm afraid I found a little obscure. She

and Miriam practically came to blows over one verse, which went, if I remember rightly, something like this:

> *Ginger Tom, with a heart of brick,*
> *Lickety-lick, lickety-lick,*
> *Heart of brick and a tail of ice,*
> *Why do I have to tell you twice?*

I think Miriam considered it too decadent, and I must say I rather agreed with her.

Our stay at the Villa Tomboli extended into months, and several more guests joined us, as Miriam's house seemed to be a customary port of call for any artistic celebrity who happened to be travelling through Italy. Raymond Curdle, the photographer, came for a week-end and stayed a fortnight, during which he did numerous studies of us all, including his famous one of Pandora Tickell which I reproduce in these pages. He was later to do the portrait of myself which I have used as a frontispiece to this book. Another visitor was Humphrey Halibutt, the novelist and playwright, whose latest drama, *The Sparkling Saucer*, had just been rather coolly received in London. I unwisely asked him about it one evening and he ended by telling me the whole plot at some length. It was all about love and physics and didn't sound my cup of tea at all. In fact, I confessed to Hester the next day that our sojourn with Miriam Boot was making me realise how very ignorant I was on a lot of matters and how much I would have to learn before

*I found Pandora Tickell a most unusual person*

I could begin to appreciate anything really intellectual.

"Never you mind, my pet," said Hester. "You may not be able to write books, but you've already done enough to fill several, and it's my guess you'll do a lot more before you've finished."

I couldn't help feeling that she was probably right, but in the meanwhile the question of what I actually should do next was becoming pressing. I could not take advantage of Miriam's hospitality for ever, and it was essential that I should soon start earning some money again. I had managed to save a certain amount from my Hollywood salary, but a good deal of that had been spent on my travels round the Continent with Blackie. Lucy had bought my house in Belgravia, which also helped, but I would have to return to London sooner or later and find somewhere to live and a new career to follow. These were the problems that were occupying my mind when Miriam announced one week-end that she was going to give a party. We were all to ask anyone we liked and it was to be her farewell to Florence for this year, as she had to return to London shortly to see her publishers, who were getting anxious about the new volume of her autobiography.

Of course Hester and I knew nobody in Florence, but she sent a message to Vera Smythe-Haddock at Santa Caterina, asking her to come.

"I don't suppose she will," said Hester, "but it's worth trying, and at least she doesn't talk about books the whole time."

Raymond Curdle announced that he was asking

*A group of guests at the Villa Tomboli (l. to r.: Pandora
Tickell, Lucian Tickell, Raymond Curdle, Humphrey
Halibutt)*

a large party of Society people from Venice, and insisted that the whole thing should be in Renaissance
fancy dress, which of course made it very easy for
Pandora Tickell and appealed to her immensely.
When we told him Vera might be coming he was
enraptured and said she would add the final touch,
"provided", as he said, "she doesn't come in mufti".

Poor Edith was kept very busy organising things
for the next few days, and I must say she did a wonderful job. I had not been at a party for months and
found myself eagerly looking forward to the appointed
evening. Little did I know that it would prove to be
yet another turning-point in my life.

We had a message back from Vera, brought by a

novice, to say that she would look in at the party for a few minutes. I was glad to know I would be seeing her again, as I felt my period of seclusion from the outside world was rapidly coming to an end, and some final words of advice from her would be very welcome.

The evening of the party finally arrived, and the guests began to assemble. Miriam Boot had managed to acquire a complete Swiss Guard's uniform, and looked quite remarkable. In fact, all the costumes were picturesque in the extreme, and Hester and I felt rather put in the shade, as all we had done was to re-style two evening dresses in the Botticelli manner, using a picture-postcard of "The Return of Spring" as our guide.

When Raymond Curdle's party from Venice turned up, I was disturbed to find that one of their number was none other than Lola Pickering. She recognised me at once and launched into a stream of gossip and reminiscence about our fellow-members in the cast of *The Princess and Me*, which I received rather coolly. While she was talking away, I became aware of her partner, a tall, aristocratic-looking Persian, who was eyeing me with obvious appreciation. Lola suddenly realised we had not been introduced.

"Oh, darling, how frightful of me!" she cried. "This is Sir Algernon Gutts-Whytyng. He's an absolute dear, aren't you, Algy?"

I shook paws with Sir Algernon, and for some reason I felt that this meeting was fraught with significance. However, he was soon carried off by Lola to

*An aristocratic-looking Persian*

meet someone else, and by this time the party had really got under way.

I don't remember the evening in much detail, I'm afraid, and in any case nothing of importance occurred until shortly after midnight, by which time everyone had consumed quite a lot of drink. Vera Smythe-Haddock was still there, having, apparently, forgotten that she had only intended to stay a few minutes, and was being persuaded by Raymond Curdle to render a saxophone solo as soon as someone could find a saxophone. Miriam was nowhere to be seen but no one was particularly concerned. Then suddenly we were all distracted from our merry-making by an uproar of shouting and banging emanating from the gazebo in the garden. The next moment Edith came careering across the lawn in floods of tears and dashed up to her room. There was still no sign of Miriam, and an attempt was made to start the party going again. But the incident had somehow damped our enthusiasm, and people began to leave shortly afterwards.

Just as Vera was departing, Edith re-appeared carrying an old suitcase and, without a word to anyone else, went over to her and asked to be taken to Santa Caterina. Vera was somewhat non-plussed, but Edith was insistent and they finally left together.

I was about to go over to Hester and suggest we went to bed, when I felt a paw on my shoulder. I turned to find Sir Algernon beside me.

"Goodnight," he said, with an inscrutable look. "We shall meet again, I hope." And with that he was gone.

I never did discover what had caused the final row between Miriam and Edith, and Miriam never referred to the matter the next day.

That evening, however, much to my surprise, she asked me if I would like to take Edith's place.

"But I can't type or do shorthand," I said.

"Never mind about that," replied Miriam. "Typists are easy to get. Just look after the social side, and see I'm not badgered. Be quite amusing for you, get to know a lot of people. Need a job, don't you?"

I confessed that I did. And so it came about that a few days later Hester and I departed for London with Miriam. I had no idea what lay ahead; but, whatever it might be, I now felt confident that I could deal with it.

# CHAPTER VII

## *Wedding bells*

How strange it was, returning to London once more, after so much had happened to me! I wanted to avoid, if possible, seeing too much of my old friends, as I had no wish to be tempted back into the Theatre again. Of course I went to see Lucy, now firmly ensconced in my little house—and very pretty she had made it too! She had just opened in a new musical comedy, *The Tom Boy*, in which she had scored another great personal success. I went to see it with Hester a few nights after our return, and I must say Lucy's performance enchanted me, particularly her number, "Dancing on the Tiles", which became such a hit. How pretty she looked, pirouetting over the roof-tops, dressed in pale pink! I couldn't help feeling slightly envious of her; but her success was well deserved, and she had always been a much better dancer than me. Not such a strong voice perhaps, but what a piquant personality!

Of course she was engaged again, this time to the editor of the *Daily Miaow*, whose name I forget. But in any case it only lasted a few weeks, as Lucy had suddenly developed an interest in politics, and she found she disliked the paper's policy so much that she couldn't bear to be associated with it. She went on at some length about free fishing rights and other things, but it was all double dutch to me, since, as long as I had my fish, I never worried particularly where it had come from. Lucy maintained that we could all have more fish at less price, if the government

*Lucy's performance enchanted me*

would let us; and I dare say she was right. But it did seem to me to be carrying it rather far when she let it interfere with her love life. And in any case, as I told her, she could now afford to pay for the most expensive fish. But I think she had got tired of her fiancé anyway, and the business over politics was just an excuse to break off the engagement.

She was very intrigued by my new job with Miriam Boot and I must say it was often very interesting and at times quite unusual. I had a room in Miriam's house in Chelsea and spent most of my day answering the telephone, receiving guests and seeing that Miriam kept all her numerous engagements. On the whole she treated me very well, and I was fortunate in that she had engaged a shorthand typist, called Myrtle, on whom she could vent her spleen if she felt like it. I was given a ticking off from time to time; but Miriam never remained annoyed with me for long, and would usually end up by pinching my tail and saying, "Ee, you're a devil, Sylvia!"—quite why I don't know —and we would both laugh, and that would be that.

The new volume of autobiography was finally completed just in time for publication, and I was kept busy by people ringing up and asking if they had been mentioned in it, and, if so, was the mention defamatory. Apparently, the ninth volume had started three lawsuits, which had cost Miriam a bit of money, but had sent the sales soaring. She was expecting at least five as a result of Volume Ten, and she instructed me to tell everyone who rang up that she had written "the whole bloody truth about every bloody thing they'd done", to use her own words. I, of course, put it a little more tactfully than that, especially when Lalage de Furrier rang up, as I already knew that Miriam had devoted several pages to accusing Miss de Furrier of lifting the plot of her first successful novel lock stock and barrel from *Jane Eyre*.

The callers at the house in Chelsea were more numerous and even more varied than the guests at the Villa Tomboli. I always kept as much in the background as I could, since I knew that I might be recognised, which could have proved embarrassing for

*A good likeness, if a little idealised*

everybody. Pandora Tickell turned up one day, having
finally extricated herself for good from Dante's Inferno,
and informed us that Miaow-Miaow Latouche was in
town for the première of *Joan of Arc* and she was
going to interview her for *Chatte*—a brilliant stunt apparently, but it all seemed rather chi-chi to me. I later
read in the papers that Pandora had quoted a good

deal of "The Chaffinch and the Cod" to Miaow-Miaow, who replied by telling her that it needed a sex-angle. So the whole interview had ended in chaos, with Pandora stumbling out of Claridges in tears and Miaow-Miaow cursing in Hungarian, or whatever her native tongue was supposed to be. Lucian Tickell was furious about it and told Miriam that Pandora had been misunderstood from the moment she was born, to which Miriam, I believe, made some ribald reply. So we didn't see the Tickells again for weeks.

Raymond Curdle also called from time to time, usually with a party of friends. He had now taken up interior decorating as a sideline and offered to do a mural in Miriam's sitting-room. I posed for one of the figures, which was meant to represent something mythical, quite what I was never sure. However, I reproduce it in this book, as it always seemed to me a good likeness, if a little idealised, and I think the costume suited me. Miriam told me privately that she wanted the mural done in a fortnight, as, once the tenth volume was published, she was sure Raymond would never speak to her again. In actual fact, when it did come out, he threatened to come round and take the wall down brick by brick and throw them at her; but she just laughed it off in her usual bluff manner, and after a few days they were the best of friends again.

All in all, the time passed pleasantly enough, and I was sufficiently absorbed in what was going on around me to be able to forget the past, or at least ignore it, and not to regret bidding farewell to my career as an actress. So that when Sir Algernon Gutts-Whytyng came into my life again, I had regained most of my self-confidence and felt more at ease with him than I had at our first encounter in Florence.

He suddenly rang me up out of the blue and asked me to dine with him. I accepted, and he took me out to Prunier's where we had a delicious meal, and he told me about his family and his country house in Essex. His father was dead, but his mother was still very much alive and sounded rather formidable. He had two sisters, Sybil and Lorna, both younger than himself—in fact Lorna had only "come out" the previous season and was considered one of the leading debutantes of the year.

It all seemed like another world to me—a world of good manners and gracious living, such as I had never known, but for which I felt a subconscious yearning, due, of course, to my own connections with the aristocracy. I asked him if he knew the Herringtons of Hakeworth, and he said he did, very well. It was on the tip of my tongue to tell him they were my grandparents; but it would have meant telling him also about Mother, and I felt we were not yet well enough acquainted.

When I rang Hester and told her about my evening's outing, she was delighted.

"Marry him, darling!" she said jubilantly, "he's just what you need and just the sort of husband I had in mind for you."

I laughed and said we were only friends, but, on thinking it over, I felt she was probably right. It seemed only fitting that, after my excursions into the professional world, I should now take what was after all, but

*Lady Gutts-Whytyng, with Sybil and Lorna*

The Wedding of the Year

for Mother's divagation, my rightful place among the aristocracy.

So when, a few weeks later, after I had been out to dinner with him several times, Sir Algernon proposed to me, I decided to accept. I have, as my readers may by now be aware, a great belief in the power of Fate, and it seemed to me at the time that this was the logical outcome of our chance meeting at Miriam's party in Florence.

When I told Miriam, she did not seem to be surprised. Instead she said once more, "Ee, you're a devil, Sylvia!" and chuckled throatily.

I had still to meet Algernon's family, and I must confess it was rather an alarming prospect. I guessed that Lady Gutts-Whytyng would have checked up on me and would be quite aware who I was. This turned out to be so, and she was no less formidable than I had imagined. But, as luck would have it, she was an ardent film fan, and had seen all my pictures, some of them more than once. She seemed much more interested in finding out all she could about Hollywood than in making sure I was a suitable bride for her son. In fact, her only reference to our proposed marriage was made just as we were leaving her house in Lowndes Square.

"Do you want to have kittens?" she said. I replied that I did, whereupon she smiled and kissed me goodbye very warmly.

Algernon's two sisters, Sybil and Lorna, were reasonably polite to me, but I found them rather conceited and not exactly brimming over with intelligence. They warmed towards me a little when they heard I had starred in a Laurence Fortescue operetta, since he was considered persona grata in Society, and hardly regarded as a "Theatrical" at all but more as a social institution.

Hester, as was to be expected, was delighted about the whole thing and immediately set about collecting my trousseau.

"You've done it at last, dearie," she said. "I'm really proud of you."

I asked Lucy to be my head bridesmaid, and she was very tickled.

"It'll be my best part yet!" she said in her light-hearted way. "What a pity there'll only be one performance!"

Sybil and Lorna were also bridesmaids, of course, and all our gowns were designed by Edwina Lessiter, who, I think, surpassed herself. As Laurence Fortescue wittily put it, we looked like "the finales of all the Fortescue operettas rolled into one". Lucy suggested he should write a number for me to sing as I came down the aisle, but I impressed upon her that I was taking my marriage very seriously and now looked upon my life in the Theatre as a thing of the distant past. I don't think she really believed me, but then she could never understand that I did not have the Theatre in my blood in quite the same way that she did.

My wedding, when it finally took place, was, as some of my readers will remember, undoubtedly the Wedding of the Year, although I say it myself. There must have been hundreds of guests and the reception at Claridges was crammed with well-known faces from the aristocracy and the Theatre. Vincent Crabbe was there, looking as magnificent as ever—*The Maid of the Miaowntains* was still running to packed houses. Laurence Fortescue was there too, exercising his usual charm on all the titled ladies. And so, I regret to say, was Lola Pickering who had somehow got herself invited, and was wearing red satin, very low-cut. It was just about the time of the diamond engagement collar affair, and old Lady Gutts-Whytyng nearly had a seizure in the receiving line when Lola's name was announced. However, I'm glad to say she behaved reasonably well, although Lucy told me later that she had dropped a lobster claw down an elderly duchess's back and caused a minor disturbance in her usual inconsiderate way.

Otherwise the whole affair went splendidly and it is a day I shall always remember. Hester wept copiously all through the service, but looked charming and renewed several old acquaintances among the Society people present. She had asked Madame Whiskeronova and her sister, although I wasn't too keen on the idea, and they turned up, looking a little out of place amongst all the others. Still, it was nice to see them again, and when Madame Alicia came to shake hands at the reception, she said in her usual loud, clear voice: "I'm glad to see you've not forgotten my deportment classes, Sylvia", which was gratifying in its way, though not, I must confess, entirely true.

Lucy, of course, looked a picture, and got on famously with the best man, Reggie Mountsalmon, a Guards officer friend of Algernon's. I'm not sure that she didn't get engaged to him at a later date, but he was posted to Cawnpore, and finally, I'm told, went native.

The papers were full of my wedding, and I believe some of the Gutts-Whytyng relations were rather incensed by the references to my past in the cheaper press. But it was too late for them to do anything about it, and Algernon and I were well away on the first part of our honeymoon tour of the Continent. How different that trip was from my previous whirlwind journey round Europe with Blackie! This time I was well and truly married to a tom whose background was beyond reproach!

My only regret about my wedding was that Mother was absent. I feel sure she would have been proud of me, and I longed for her to see me restored to my rightful place among the aristocracy. I did receive another postcard from her on my wedding morning, this time with a coloured photograph of Shanghai and the usual brief message: "Congratulations to my little daughter. I and your new stepfather, Mr Chow Min, send fondest love." I decided not to put this in with the telegrams to be read out at the reception, as I felt the Gutts-Whytyngs would not have reacted very favourably. When I showed the card to Hester, she said that Mother must be working her way gradually westwards and would probably turn up in London in a few years' time.

Our honeymoon lasted three months and took us to most of Europe's beauty spots. We spent a day or two in Florence and I made a "sentimental journey" to Santa Caterina, where I received a warm welcome from Vera Smythe-Haddock. Edith had, apparently, taken to nunnery life as a duck takes to water, but Vera thought it inadvisable for us to meet in case the encounter revived unhappy memories of her experiences at the Villa Tomboli.

We returned to London in time for the start of the season and what a season it was! Our marriage had been considered the most romantic event of the year, and we were asked everywhere—in fact, it was not unusual for us to go to as many as three functions in the same evening. At first I sensed a certain coldness towards me among the more "starchy" members of the aristocracy, but they soon warmed to me when they realised that I was by nature already "one of them".

My relations with Algernon's family were on the whole very cordial. Old Lady Gutts-Whytyng often asked me round for afternoon milk on my own, and we would chat away happily about the films she had seen recently. She was an ardent fan of Red Flounder and had seen his latest vehicle, *The Massacre of Mouse Gap*, seven times, so she was particularly interested to hear my impressions of him when we were working together in Hollywood.

Sybil and Lorna, on the other hand, I never really got to know, which was not, in my opinion, my fault. I think perhaps they envied me for the romantic life I had led, and this was borne out when Sybil suddenly eloped with the band-leader from the Pussyfoot Club, a very common ginger tom called Ned Roach. His band was known as the Happy Hell-Cats and certainly played very well; but the whole thing caused a great scandal at the time and brought to my mind

*Ned Roach of the Pussyfoot Club*

the similar escapades of Mother in her youth—although, of course, in those days such incidents were less remarkable and didn't cause the upset they do now, when everyone is so much more strait-laced. I couldn't help sympathising with Sybil, especially when the marriage went on the rocks a year later and she was stranded in Lisbon with only a small wardrobe and her tiara. Algernon flew out to fetch her home and the whole thing was forgotten as quickly as possible.

Otherwise life was going along very smoothly, and I was rapidly making a wide circle of friends in London society. I was asked to sit on the committees of one or two charities, and I played a large part in organising the famous Midnight Gala at the Felix in aid of the Home for Kittens of Unmarried Working Cats, that vast institution near Reading which does so much to alleviate an ever-growing social problem. I was instrumental in enlisting the aid of several theatrical celebrities, and was finally prevailed upon by the other members of the committee to appear myself and sing "This is Goodbye" from *That Old Fragrance* with Laurence Fortescue conducting the orchestra. I was not over-anxious to appear on the stage again, and I don't think Algernon was very pleased with the idea. But, as it all turned out, it was the success of the evening, and I must confess that I received an enormous thrill from this brief return to "the boards" and from the ovation which the audience kindly gave me.

This reappearance on the stage led to my being asked by the B.B.C. to appear in a television panel game, "What's Your Tail?" Again I was hesitant about accepting, but Hester urged me to do it.

*"What's Your Tail?"*

"You've still got a duty to the public, love," she told me, "and this way you can fulfil it without being undignified. Being an aristocrat is all very well, but remember you're still a performer too."

So, after getting Algernon's rather reluctant consent, I took my place on the panel, and, much to my surprise, found myself scoring points in every programme. The game was simple enough—almost childish in my opinion—but it seemed to please the viewers, and old Lady Gutts-Whytyng said that it was one of the few programmes which kept her away from the pictures.

When I had been appearing in "What's Your Tail?" for a few weeks, I was approached by the *Daily Miaow* to write a weekly column, and that was the beginning of "Lady Sylvia's Secrets" in which, every Thursday, I dispensed to my female readers various hints and suggestions for attaining success in Society and also in their love-lives. The column was very popular, but not with Algernon, who from time to time suggested I should give it up. However, I persisted, and later, when my life once again took on a new pattern, I was glad of the literary experience it had afforded me.

But that is looking ahead. For the moment all was well with me, and when, in the New Year, I found that I was about to become a mother, my happiness was complete.

# CHAPTER VIII

# The Gutts-Whytyng divorce and after

Motherhood, it is generally agreed, is quite an undertaking. But I was prepared to devote myself to it as freely as I had to my stage and film career. In fact, the prospect of having kittens thrilled me just as much as any first night. Algernon insisted that I should go to the family seat, Whytyng Manor, in Essex, to await my children's birth, and I agreed to do so, although I would rather have remained in town, where I could call on Hester if I felt like it; she had been with me in every crisis so far, and it seemed wrong to me that she should not be there for the arrival of my first kittens. However, I deferred to Algernon's wishes, and on a windy day in March, in the depths of the Essex countryside, my first family was born. There were three of them, two girls and a boy, and I thought they were beautiful; but I'm afraid my feelings were not shared by my husband and his family. Algernon was the first to see them, and he was reasonably polite; but old Lady Gutts-Whytyng made no effort to conceal her disapproval, and Sybil and Lorna were positively rude. For my first family consisted of a grey girl, like myself (nothing wrong there), a tabby (long-haired, which is something after all), and a ginger tom. But not one of them was a full Persian, and although I myself thought, and still think, that they were perfectly sweet, to the Gutts-Whytyngs they were quite "beyond the pale" and the whole marriage had been proved to be a dreadful mistake. I can only assume that they had taken me for a full Persian myself, and I suppose I ought to have admitted the truth about Mother's unfortunate liaison; but, whatever they had thought about me in the first place, from the moment my kittens were born I knew that I was no longer considered "one of them" and my marriage, which had at first been so successful, now began to disintegrate. I did make some effort to pin a little of the blame on to Algernon. After all, there was no reason to assume that I was *entirely* responsible for the colour of my kittens, and there might have been a slip in the Gutts-Whytyng family which nobody knew about. But old Lady Gutts-Whytyng wouldn't hear of it, and refused even to see my kittens again. Algernon made an attempt to be kind to me, but I knew that all was really over between us and I longed for Hester to come and comfort me. However, I put a brave face on it and insisted that my children should at least be christened. I chose their names, Maxine, Audrey and Joe—none of them Gutts-Whytyng family names but by that time I was past caring. As soon as I was up and about, I made Algernon take me and the kittens back to town, and I determined that, whatever the Gutts-Whytyngs might think of them, I was not going to show the slightest trace of shame. I rang up Hester and asked her to tell the newspapers all about them, and then I had a large party and invited all my theatrical and literary friends. We had a simply hilarious evening (Algernon went to his club), and everyone was mad about the kittens. As soon as Lucy saw them she said that next time she got engaged she really must go through with it as motherhood was obviously *the* thing. She was just about to go off to New York for the

American production of *The Tom Boy* and I advised her to get married there, as Americans don't make such a fuss about breeding and no one would mind if she had nothing but ginger toms.

Hester was, of course, quite entranced with my little family and immediately became their unofficial granny. Miriam was grudging about them and said that kittens were "a bloody nuisance"; but I could see she really envied me and adored them as much as everybody else. The Press came and took photographs of me and the kittens, and the next day, to my delight, our picture was in all the papers. I'm sure the Gutts-Whytyngs were furious.

Under the circumstances I realised that sooner or later Algernon and I would have to part, and I was just wondering how this could be accomplished in an amicable manner, when once again Fate took the decision out of my paws.

A week or so after the party, Hester rang me up and asked me if I had seen the latest issue of *The Catler*—that well-known journal which keeps the public informed about the doings of the aristocracy. As it happened, I had not, and so she told me that she had just seen something in it which she thought I should know about. It turned out to be a photograph of Algernon and Sonia Grimsby, taken at the Pussyfoot Club. I don't suppose I need to tell my readers who Sonia Grimsby was—or indeed still is—but just in case, I had better remind them that she had, at the time of which I am speaking, just returned to England after divorcing a well-known Hollywood star because his mouse-hunting trips interfered with her social life. Previous to that

*Something which she thought I should know about*

she had been married to a French marquis and a Persian prince. It now looked as if she were setting her cap at Algernon, and various other pieces of information which came to my ears soon confirmed this suspicion. When I finally faced Algernon with my evidence, I forebore to point out to him that she was no more a full Persian than I am, which I thought was magnanimous of me; but I was only concerned in clearing up the situation between us and using Sonia Grimsby as a means of securing a divorce on the best possible terms for myself and my dear kittens. This probably sounds very mercenary in cold print, but I would like to remind my readers, especially those who are mothers, how deeply one's feelings can be hurt by an insult to one's kittens—and these were the first I had ever had.

My next step was to pack up my belongings and move to Lucy's house in Belgravia with the kittens. She had departed for New York, but had told me that the house was at my disposal any time I cared to use it —I think perhaps she had foreseen the turn of events.

So I established myself there, and awaited the divorce proceedings.

Not surprisingly the case caused a great sensation and was fully—sometimes too fully—reported in the press. All society was shocked by the sudden disruption of what had seemed to be an ideal marriage, and one old duchess was heard to suggest that Sonia Grimsby should be run out of the country. One afternoon old Lady Gutts-Whytyng came to see me and pleaded with me to drop the whole case and be reconciled with Algernon. I think she missed me very much, as there was now no one with whom she could discuss the films she had seen, and Sybil was proving particularly trying after her unfortunate elopement. But I was adamant, even when she produced a small parcel of lobster for the kittens, which she had purchased at Fortnum's, and told her that I had no intention of returning to Algernon. I'm sure she disliked Sonia Grimsby as much as everyone else did, and knew that she wouldn't have any kittens at all, which would be one worse than my assorted bunch.

The divorce finally came through without any serious incidents, and Hester said my behaviour on the stand was quite exemplary, which was probably due to my having played a very similar part in *Cat's Cradle*, my last Hollywood film. I dressed very discreetly for the occasion, with the minimum of jewellery, and, although Algernon's counsel made great play with my admittedly colourful past, I quite won the judge's heart and ended by having things all my own way.

As I expect most people know, Sonia Grimsby

*Discreetly dressed for the occasion*

never did marry Algernon, and I must say I was glad, if only for the sake of old Lady Gutts-Whytyng, who, I'm sure, would never have survived another mésalliance in the family. Instead she went off to the South of France with a party of people which included Lola Pickering and, I believe, the editor of the *Daily Miaow*, who had gone a little off the rails since Lucy broke off their engagement. I heard rumours of rather disgraceful goings-on in Cap Ferrat, including a frightful brawl in the Souris Blanc between Lola and Sonia Grimsby, reputedly over Algernon. But by that time none of it concerned me. Lola and Sonia were both bad hats, and they could have jumped off Cap Ferrat into the sea, for all I cared.

Now that I was free again I had to make new plans for the future, and this time I had three small mouths to feed, in addition to my own. I had, of course, been awarded a respectable alimony; but it was not really enough to live on, and besides I had an urge to do something active as well as looking after my kittens.

Miriam offered to give me back my old job, and for a time I considered taking it on again. But I decided in the end that I must go forward to something new, and for this reason I also turned down an offer from Laurence Fortescue to appear in his new show, although I was flattered that he still considered I might be of value to him. I had, of course, left the panel of "What's Your Tail?" when my kittens were about to be born; and it seemed unlikely that I would be asked to return now that I had severed my connections with the aristocracy. But I resumed writing my column, now calling it "Sylvia's Secrets", and it was even more successful than before owing to the publicity I had received from my divorce. I now included hints on bringing up kittens, and Maxine, Audrey and Joe were soon almost as well known to the public as myself, largely due, of course, to Raymond Curdle's famous photograph of us all together, which I reproduce in these pages. And, although I say it myself, they were quite unusual kittens, very advanced for their age, and each possessing a personality all its own. Maxine was always very like myself, both in looks and character, and she has inherited my love of the Theatre. Audrey was remarkably pretty, even as a tiny kitten, and will, I think, grow up to be one of the beauties of her day, like her grandmother before her. And Joe—well, Joe, was a ginger tom and he has all the dash and energy one associates with his colouring; he might grow up to be anything, and already he has an eye for the ladies and a way with him that will break many a girl's heart before he is much older.

But I am running ahead once again. At the time

*Me and the kittens (Raymond Curdle's photograph)*

I am speaking of they were still in their cradles, and I was once again a single cat, trying to establish a life of my own and make a fresh future for myself. Strangely enough, it was in an entirely new sphere that I eventually found my métier, and this I owe largely to Lucy Trembath and the fact that I was now living in her house. Lucy, my readers will remember, had recently developed an interest in politics, and by the time she left for America with *The Tom Boy*, she had made friends with a number of Cabinet Ministers and Members of Parliament. They used to foregather regularly at the Belgravia house of an evening and discuss the issues of the day, while Lucy dispensed crab and cream and, if the argument became too heated, cleared the atmosphere by sitting down at her baby grand and rendering a song number from one of her successes. These sessions ceased of course when Lucy left London; but, quite by chance, the Foreign Secretary, whose name I prefer not to mention, rang up one day to ask after her. He had been away at a Five-Power Conference at the time of Lucy's departure and thought she was still in London. However, he was so charming over the telephone and sounded so disappointed when I told him Lucy was away that I decided on the spur of the moment to ask him to call one evening and bring any odd under-secretary or attaché who happened to be free. I then rang Hester and told her what I had done, and she was all for it. Between us we arranged a simple little soirée, which turned out to be a great success. I followed Lucy's example, and sang one or two songs from my shows, including "Whose Kitten Are You?" which went down very well, and the Foreign Secretary was quite delighted with the whole affair—so much so that he asked me when he might come again, as he was sure the Prime Minister would also enjoy it. So, almost without realising it, I was launched on a new career as a political hostess. Of course it meant a lot of work, including the acquisition of a reasonable knowledge of political affairs, which obliged Hester and myself to read *The Times* aloud to each other every day and memorise the salient points in the Parliamentary debates. Hester became very enthusiastic and got quite carried away over a bill to abolish the licensing hours. Unfortunately she chose to address her most persuasive remarks to an elderly M.P. from Bedfordshire who was a famous teetotaller, and there would have been an ugly scene

*"Bye, Bye, Blackbird" in harmony*

had I not nipped smartly over to the piano and launched into vocal gems from *That Old Fragrance*.

Our little parties were predominantly male gatherings. But occasionally a lady M.P. would join us, and although I found them rather dull creatures, there was the odd exception, like Bella Whaylebone, Socialist M.P. for Basingstoke, who could always be relied upon to add to the evening's gaiety. She had something of the same forthright qualities as Miriam Boot but a great warm-heartedness as well, and, although I could not agree with many of her political views, as a person I took to her at once. She had been a music-hall artist in her younger days, and I remember one evening when she and Hester gave a rendering of "Bye, Bye, Blackbird" in harmony, which not only delighted the assembly but also woke up all the kittens, who insisted on being brought downstairs to hear the encore. Unfortunately, Bella Whaylebone became rather militant one night over the question of equal pay for lady cats in the Civil Service, and ended up by throwing a dish of crab mayonnaise at the Prime

Minister, so from then on we had to be careful not to invite them on the same evening. I also had a little difficulty with a tempestuous member of the Opposition who wanted me to assist him in his campaign for non-interference in Siam, and I eventually had to explain to him that my knowledge of Siamese Cats was limited to *The Princess and Me*, which I think must have upset him a little, as he never came to the house again. I never could understand why he thought the Siamese were so hard done by, as I have always found that they are treated with even more respect than Persians, and certainly Get Yû was adored by everyone who worked with her. But of course she was an exceptional creature and had such wonderful top notes.

So my life gradually took on a new pattern and I once more felt myself established in a new environment and with a new circle of friends. As well as writing my column for the *Daily Miaow*, I also turned out odd articles for *Chatte* and similar magazines—usually based on my past experiences in the worlds of the Theatre, the Cinema and High Society. In fact it was

*A tempestuous member of the Opposition*

*He nearly convinced her
that she had a Jocasta complex*

these articles, coupled with the urging of my friends, that first gave me the idea of writing my memoirs. But I knew that would be a big undertaking, and I decided to postpone it at least until I had a proper home of my own and my kittens were more able to look after themselves. The question of somewhere to live became more urgent that autumn, as I had a letter from Lucy saying that she would be coming back to London for Christmas, which meant that I would have to move out of the Belgravia house. She had had a great success in New York and had got herself engaged to a big film executive; but he had turned out to be completely under the thumb of his psycho-analyst, who had started on Lucy as well. She had had one or two sessions with him just to please her fiancé, but one afternoon he nearly convinced her that she had a Jocasta complex and she decided it was high time she called the whole thing off.

So, as soon as her show closed, she intended returning to London.

I could see that, with my limited income, I would have some difficulty in finding a house in London to accommodate myself and my growing family, and I was considering the idea of taking a cottage in the country, when my life was changed once again by one of those chance meetings which have played so great a part in shaping my existence. And at this point I feel that, if only to safeguard my present happiness, I should draw a slight veil of reticence over this narrative. For the particular meeting I refer to, which took place at one of our political evenings, led eventually to my second, and I firmly believe last, marriage. Suffice it to say that my husband-to-be, whom I shall simply refer to as N—,—, was brought along one night by the Minister for Agriculture and Fisheries, with whom he had been in consultation over a big deal with Scandinavia for the importation of skate—a vital move in fact in the campaign which had meant so much to Lucy and had driven her to break off her engagement to the editor of the *Daily Miaow*.

All I need say is that in a matter of days I realised that I no longer needed to concern myself with finding a new home. When Lucy eventually returned from New York I was already established in the charming house in Surrey, where, in my own cosy little study, I am now sitting and writing the concluding chapters of these memoirs.

# CHAPTER IX

## *The tail ends*

The time is fast approaching for me to lay down my pen and submit these memoirs of mine to the judgment of the world. They will, I'm afraid, anger some people; but others, I hope, they will please. I can only say that they present the truth about myself, unvarnished and unadorned, and if they cause offence, I apologise; but at the same time I can honestly say that there is nothing in these pages of which I am ashamed or which I regret having written. In fact, on reflection, I feel I have a great deal to be proud of, and, whatever else people may say about me, no one can deny that I have, as I mentioned in my first chapter, lived my lives to the full. In fact, I feel justified in my present retirement from public life, though there is no saying when I might once more be tempted to seek the limelight either as an actress or else in some entirely new capacity.

*I shall simply refer to him as N——*

But at the moment I am content to live a quiet life with N——, in Surrey and watch my kittens growing up around me. Next autumn, Maxine enrols at Madame Whiskeronova's, and I have high hopes that she will one day be a star and perhaps outshine her own mother. Audrey is in her last term at Rodine and will soon be having her first London season; if she doesn't turn out to be the debutante of the year I shall be very surprised. Joe is going into the Navy and looks very dashing and handsome in his cadet's uniform; it goes without saying that he will have a sweetheart in every port. Yes, I think I can be proud of my little family. Whatever the Gutts-Whytyngs may have thought of them at birth I am sure that, could they see my kittens now, they would regret having so readily disowned them.

Hester is still comfortably installed in Dolphin Square and comes down to visit me at week-ends. The last time she was here we were reminiscing about the past and she said to me, in her usual sage way, "Well, ducks, I was right, wasn't I? Your ginger streak certainly wasn't a handicap—in fact it put you right on top, you mark my words."

I couldn't help agreeing with her, for, although my mixed breeding did cost me a title, it gave me the guts and the independence to make my way in the world, often against great odds. And I no longer resent the fact that Mother failed to give me a pure pedigree. Dear Mother! She has still not returned to England. The last words I had was a postcard from Kashmir with a photograph of a Rajah's palace and the simple message on the back: "My bedroom is marked with

*Miaow-Miaow Latouche in CinemaScope*

an X. Your ever loving Mother." But one day I hope
she will be reunited with her daughter and lay eyes on
the grandchildren she has never seen. And by that
time, I am happy to say, there will be more grandchildren for her to lay eyes on. For in a few weeks'
time, if all goes well, Maxine, Audrey and Joe will
have some little brothers and sisters.

I still see something of my old associates. Lucy, in
particular, has remained a loyal friend, and I always
pay her a call on the odd occasions when I am up in
town. She is also Maxine's godmother and will, I'm
sure, be generous with advice and help, when the time
comes for Maxine to start on her stage career. At the
moment she is starring in a revival of *Pussy, Be Good!*
at the Felix. N—— and I went the other evening, and
Lucy has lost none of her old magic. Her love-life still
has its ups and downs, but at the time of writing she
is not engaged to anybody, though I imagine that state
of affairs won't last for long.

Miriam has just published her eleventh volume of autobiography and it has caused the usual furore. I believe the Tickells have rushed into print about it, but I must confess I have only read one chapter—the one that mentions me—and I was relieved to find that Miriam had dealt with me very kindly.

Vincent Crabbe, as everyone knows, is still starring successfully in his popular musical plays. Whenever we meet, which is only occasionally nowadays, we still laugh about the time when he suddenly found himself playing opposite me. Laurence Fortescue also carries on with his operettas, though the last one was not, I'm afraid, a great success. I was at the first night with N——— and there in the stage box was Laurence with, as always, old Mrs Fortescue, Edwina, Geoffrey and Madge.

Of my Hollywood associates I only know what I read in the papers, and they don't seem to have changed much from the time when I knew them and worked with them. The other day I saw Miaow-Miaow Latouche in CinemaScope, and I have to confess that it seemed to me altogether too much of a good—or should I say bad—thing. However, she has managed to retain her position as a star, and one cannot but admire such tenacity.

I hear the car coming up the drive, which means that N——— has arrived back from the City. His deal with Scandinavia went through successfully and I and my family possess every comfort a cat could wish for. Yes, indeed, my existence nowadays is remarkably placid after the turbulent times I have experienced. No one, to look at me now, would think—but then I wouldn't particularly want them to. All that is in the past. As to the present, I am very contented. But as far as the future is concerned—well, nine lives take a lot of living, and, as Hester said to me the other day, "You never know, my pet, you may only have got as far as number eight!"